ABOUT GOD AND HIS WAYS

ABOUT GOD AND HIS WAYS

By LAWRIE HAMILTON
Illustrated by ATI FORBERG
GUSTAV K. WIENCKE, Editor

LUTHERAN CHURCH PRESS/Philadelphia

LCA SUNDAY CHURCH SCHOOL SERIES

This pupil's Reader is accompanied by a pupil's Workbook and by a Teacher's Guide, *Friends of Jesus*. This material has been prepared for use in Term 1 in the Sunday church school (2-1). The theme for the year is developed as follows: TERM 1, Friends of Jesus Wonder *About God and His Ways;* TERM 2, Friends of Jesus Find Out *How God Wants Us to Live;* TERM 3, Friends of Jesus Become *Helpers in the Church.* All materials for the course are listed in the Teacher's Guide.

COPYRIGHT © 1967. Lutheran Church Press. All rights reserved. Book design by LOU DAY. Printed in U.S.A.
16-127   9841H66

Contents

For Parents   7

1   I WONDER ABOUT THE WORLD GOD MADE
- I Wonder Why   11
- Who Lives in the Pond?   15
- How Did God Make the World?   23
- I Wonder About the Stars   32

2   I WONDER ABOUT GOD AND ME
- I Wonder If God Knows Me   39
- If I Weren't Me   45

3   I WONDER ABOUT WHEN I DO WRONG
- "I Will Not Leave You"   51

4   I WONDER ABOUT ANSWERS TO PRAYER
- How Jesus Wants Us to Pray   62
- Wondering About God   67
- Make Someone Stop   72

5   I WONDER WHY CHRISTIANS ARE GLAD AT CHRISTMAS
- The Broken Star   79
- God's Angel Told Us   86
- The King's Star   94

6   I WONDER ABOUT THINGS NOBODY TELLS ME
- What God Looks Like   102
- How Jesus' Promise Comes True   109
- I Wonder About Heaven   118
- Songs and Prayers   123

FOR PARENTS:

Listen carefully to your child and you will discover that he is already something of a theologian. He has questions about God. He tries to fit his preschool ideas about God into the bigger world he enters now that his formal education has begun.

Perhaps he brings to you some of these questions, or "tell me why" requests, or his wondering thoughts. And you try to answer the questions or help him find some answers. But at times you admit you really do not know.

Now every question, every "I wonder" thought, is not only an opportunity to learn but also a chance to widen and strengthen your child's attitude toward God as the center of all of life. An encyclopedia can give some scientific or factual explanations, but you as an adult Christian can help your child fit his world into one piece, shaped by a growing faith in God, wise Creator, dependable Sustainer, loving and forgiving Father.

Read the stories and look at the illustrations in this book with your child. Ask your child to sing the songs at the end of the book and use the prayers, too.

1
I WONDER ABOUT THE WORLD GOD MADE

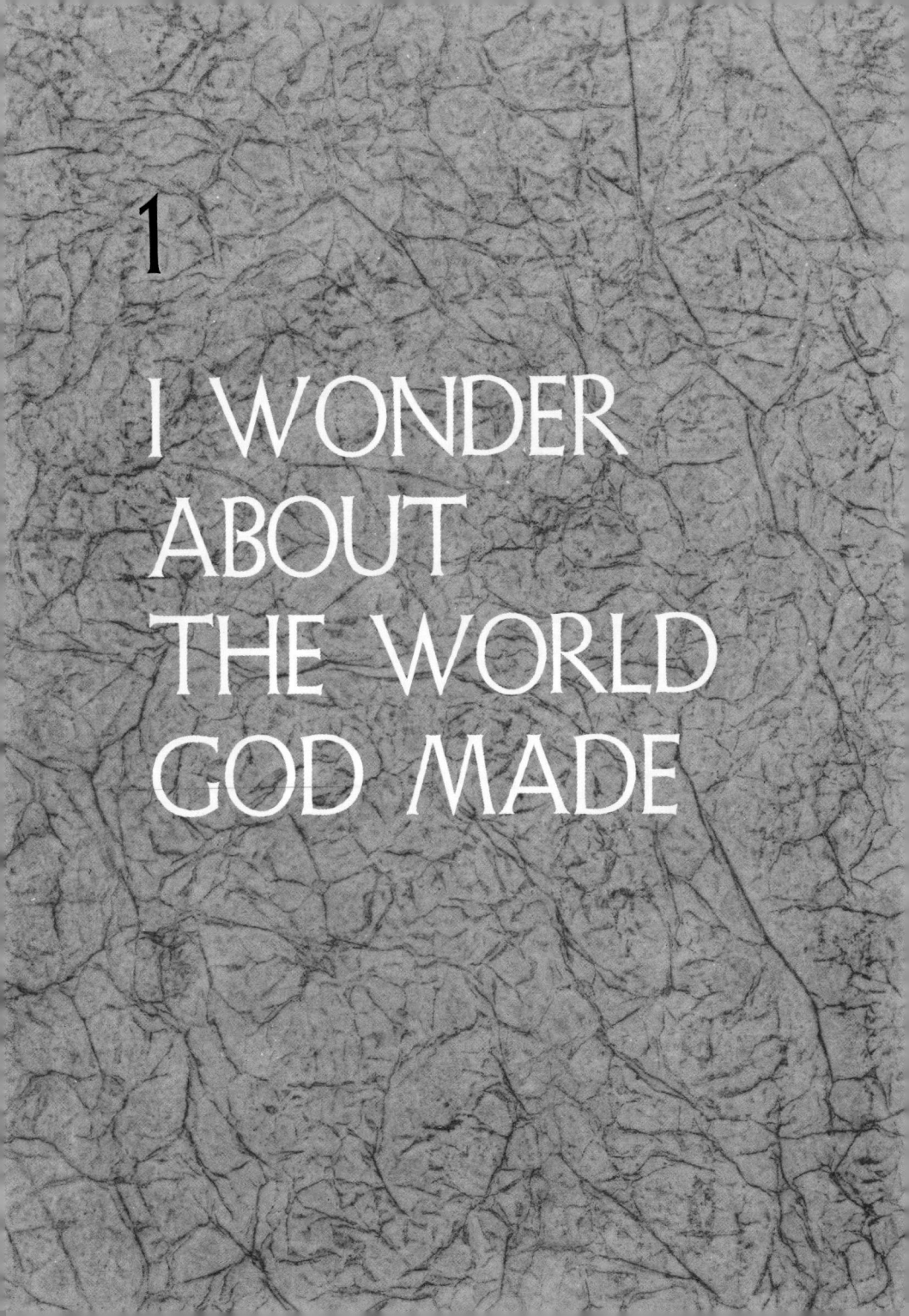

I Wonder Why

Jane liked a long, warm, lazy afternoon when she didn't have to do anything special. Then she could do her favorite thing in a place that was all her own.

Jane climbed a little hill to a quiet, grassy spot under a big oak tree. She lay down on her back and looked up at the sky and began to wonder. This was what she liked to do best.

The sky was very blue and Jane wondered, "How can the same sky be a different blue on different days?"

She turned her head to see all the sky. Behind the big old tree she saw a dark cloud coming closer and closer. "I wonder what keeps clouds up in the air," Jane thought. The cloud looked like a big horse, and then it changed to look like a mountain.

High up in the tree Jane saw three robins sitting in a row on a thin branch. It bent and swayed in the wind.

"I wonder how birds can hold on. Aren't they scared?" Jane wondered. "I wonder how God thought of so many kinds of birds."

Suddenly Jane could not see anything. Something big and yellow covered her eyes and tickled her nose. It was a big yellow leaf from the tree, and

the wind was blowing more leaves off the tree. Jane pushed the leaf away and watched red and yellow leaves go sailing by.

"I wonder why summer has to end," Jane wondered. "God, why do you make winter come now?" she said.

The big dark cloud now almost covered the sky.

The blue was gone and the sky had become grey.

Then Jane heard raindrops rustle in the leaves. A drop of rain splashed on her face.

"Why do you have to make it rain, God?" she said.

Jane stopped doing her favorite thing and went into the house to see what Grandmother was doing. Sometimes Jane liked to talk to Grandmother about things she wondered about.

You can go on an exploring hike outdoors and wonder about things you see. And you can tell someone about the things you wonder about.

Who Lives in the Pond?

Jane hurried to Denny's house next door. She carried a plastic dish.

"What is that for?" Denny asked.

"My mother gave it to me," Jane said. "It's old and scratched up."

"What do you want to do with it?"

"My mother said I could keep a pet in it," Jane said.

"Where are you going to find a pet small enough to live in that dish?" Denny asked.

"We can look around at the pond," Jane said.

Jane and Denny hurried to the pond. Not many people went there because cattails grew all around it and the ground was muddy. Denny led the way carefully into the cattails.

"Maybe we can catch a snake," Denny said.

"A snake!" Jane said. "Even if I couldn't have any other pet, I wouldn't want a snake."

Just then there was a loud rustle in the cattails. Jane stood still. So did Denny.

A flock of blackbirds flew away with a flapping noise. On each bird's wing was a bright patch of red.

"Boy!" Jane said. "I was afraid it was a snake."

"Oh, a snake can make a good pet," Denny said, "but you have to get one that isn't poisonous."

Jane got to the water first. Denny was right behind.

Splash! Splish! Plop! Frogs jumped into the water. Turtles slipped off their lily pads.

With a splash and a whoosh, ducks flew away. Then the pond looked as if no one lived there at all.

Denny came out of the cattails.

"See," he said, "there's nothing here."

"We scared everyone away," Jane said. "Let's be quiet and maybe they will come back."

Denny and Jane crawled out on a tree branch that grew out over the water. They waited quietly.

"Look at the dragonfly," Jane said. "I can see through its wings."

"There must be a million of them," Denny said. Red dragonflies were flying close to the water. Their wings shone like mirrors in the sun.

"You could catch one of them," Denny said.

"But it couldn't live in my dish. And I don't have a cage," Jane said. "Anyway, I wouldn't know what to give a dragonfly to eat."

Denny was watching some black water beetles chasing around on the water.

Suddenly he saw an animal he had never seen before.

"Look! What's that?" he whispered. He pointed to a long, thin animal with four small legs and a long tail. It was a salamander. The animal was resting on a pile of leaves and sticks.

"He would be a good pet if we could catch him," Jane said.

Denny edged back along the branch and dropped down quietly as far away from the salamander as he could. It did not move. Denny crept up on his hands and knees behind the salamander.

He reached out and grabbed it. "Good," he said.

But the slippery salamander wiggled out of Denny's hands and into the water.

"He got away!" Denny said. "He was all wet and I couldn't hold on to him."

"He would have been fun to keep as a pet," Jane said. "Let's be quiet again. Maybe he will come back. Or maybe we'll see a frog or a turtle. They are easier to catch."

Denny and Jane sat by the pond and waited.

After awhile a green frog hopped up on a log in the water. Soon other frogs came out and were sunning themselves on nearly every log.

But they were all far out in the water.

The frogs croaked and some of them hopped off their logs into the water. None of them swam closer to shore.

"How can we catch a frog?" Denny wondered.

"They would be hard to keep as pets, anyway."

Jane saw something move slowly. A large turtle climbed up on an old log. Middle-sized turtles climbed up on their favorite stones.

And some of the smallest turtles swam toward the shore and rested in the mud, half underwater.

Denny didn't move. "'Let's catch a turtle," he whispered.

"OK," whispered Jane. "Turtles are good pets."

Both stood up very slowly and moved toward the shore without a sound.

Jane saw a turtle starting to go back into the water. Quickly she ran to it. Very carefully and gently she picked up the turtle by its shell.

"I caught one!" she cried.

"I got one, too," Denny said. "Turtles are easier to catch than that slippery animal that got away."

Jane and Denny put the turtles into the dish.

"Let's put in some water for our new pets," Jane said. She filled the dish with pond water while Denny held the two turtles. Then Denny found some small stones and made an island in the dish.

"Our two turtles will be good pets," Jane said.

"I'm going to find out how to take care of turtles," said Denny. "We can give our turtles just the things they need in God's plan."

Each kind of God's creatures grows in a different way and needs special things to live. You can find out what God planned for animals who live near you.

> *The earth is full of God's creatures.*
> *Psalm 104:24*

How Did God Make the World?

Imagine a great, wide sea and high, empty mountains. No fish swim in the sea. No seaweed grows there. No birds fly over the land. No trees grow; no grass covers the ground.

Long, long ago that is how the earth looked. Men who study how life began cannot be sure what the earth looked like then because the beginning was millions of years ago. No people were there to see it. But scientists think that the world was like this before there was any living thing.

The first living things God made swam in the wide sea. They were very, very tiny. God made these tiny sea animals grow and change slowly.

Thousands and millions of years went by. Little by little the tiny animals became bigger and more like some of the animals in the ocean today. Starfish and sponges lived in the water; jellyfish and animals with shells were there.

Then God made something very important happen. God made the first fish grow and swim in the sea. Fish were a new kind of animal. Fish are not like starfish because fish have backbones.

After a time the sea was full of many different kinds of fish, but the land was still almost empty of living things.

Some of the first animals to move from the sea to the land looked like young crocodiles. They lived along the shores of the sea.

Plants, too, began to spread from the sea to the land.

Then it was time in God's plan for a new kind of animal called amphibians. They lived part of the time in water and part of the time on land.

A frog is one kind of amphibian. First it lives as a tadpole in water. Then the tadpole becomes a frog and lives on land.

Now the land was not as empty as it had been.

Besides amphibians, ferns grew as tall as trees and giant insects lived on the land. Imagine what the earth probably looked like then! But there were still no rabbits or squirrels, dogs or cats, cows or horses.

Again millions of years went by. Now life on earth looked very strange, for dinosaurs walked the earth. Some dinosaurs were as small as birds. Others became the largest land animals ever to walk the earth. The mightiest dinosaurs are called *Tyrannosaurus rex*.

The dinosaurs roamed the earth for almost 100 million years. Then they began to die, one by one. The weather became colder and colder. The dinosaurs could not keep warm or hunt for food in the icy cold that came.

Another part of God's wonderful plan began in the time of the dinosaurs. Warm-blooded animals whose body temperature stayed almost the same in cold and warm weather appeared. These animals are called mammals. Mammals have larger brains than the dinosaurs and the other animals did.

Dogs and cats, lions and elephants are mammals.

If you could have seen the earth in the time of the first mammals, it would not have looked very different from the way it looks now. But there were still no people anywhere on the whole earth.

After millions of years, the time came in God's plan for people to be born. Human beings are different from all other living things God made because God made us able to learn about his world and to know him.

God made us able to love each other and to love him.

In the beginning of the Bible you can read a verse about God and the world you live in.

> *And God saw everything that he had made, and behold, it was very good.*
>   *Genesis 1:31*

I Wonder About the Stars

On a clear, dark night the sky sparkles with stars.

Did you ever try to count the brightest stars? In between are many more stars that do not seem so bright. If you look through a telescope, you can see many more stars. The bigger the telescope, the more stars you can see. There are more than anyone can count!

Stars are some of the most wonderful things you can see. Did you know that . . .

Stars are huge balls of terribly hot fire.

They look small only because they are far, far away.

Stars shine in the daytime, too, even though you cannot see them. The sun is so bright that it seems there are no stars in the daytime. But if you could look up through a tall smokestack, you could see the stars on a sunny day!

Our sun is a star, too!

Our earth is a planet. There are other planets near us; Venus and Mars and Jupiter are planets you can see easily. They look like stars in the night sky. The moon is not a planet because it does not move around the sun as our earth does. It moves around the earth and looks very bright because it is much nearer to our earth than any planet or star.

Far, far away there are millions of planets, very much like our earth. They are near other stars.

Did you ever wonder if people live on other planets? Perhaps they do, but they may be not just like us. Nobody knows, but someday, perhaps, people will find out.

You can be sure about one thing. If people do live on other planets, they belong to God, too. God made them, just as he made us!

On a bright summer day, the sky is a rich blue. Then at night it looks like deep black water with lights shining on it.

Have you ever wanted to touch the sky? What might it feel like if you could?

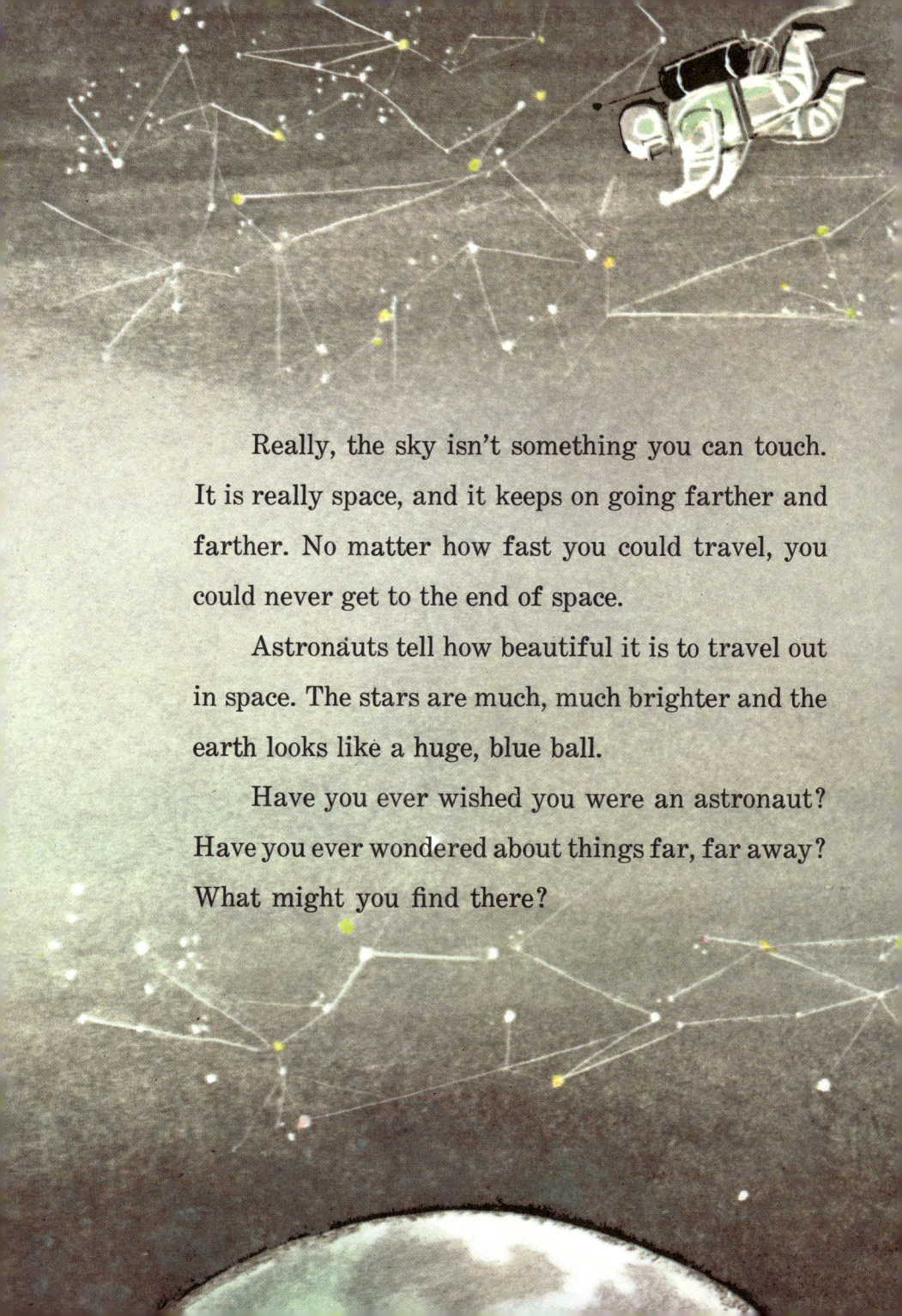

Really, the sky isn't something you can touch. It is really space, and it keeps on going farther and farther. No matter how fast you could travel, you could never get to the end of space.

Astronauts tell how beautiful it is to travel out in space. The stars are much, much brighter and the earth looks like a huge, blue ball.

Have you ever wished you were an astronaut? Have you ever wondered about things far, far away? What might you find there?

God made the billions of stars out in space. He made the earth where we live. He made our sun and moon and the planets.

But before there were any stars . . . or planets, or sun and moon . . . God was. God has always been alive. He will always be alive.

People everywhere have wondered about stars and planets and space. Space explorers will find out more than people ever knew, but they cannot find out all about God. But you can be sure that what the Bible says about God is true.

From everlasting to everlasting thou art God.
Psalm 90:2

2

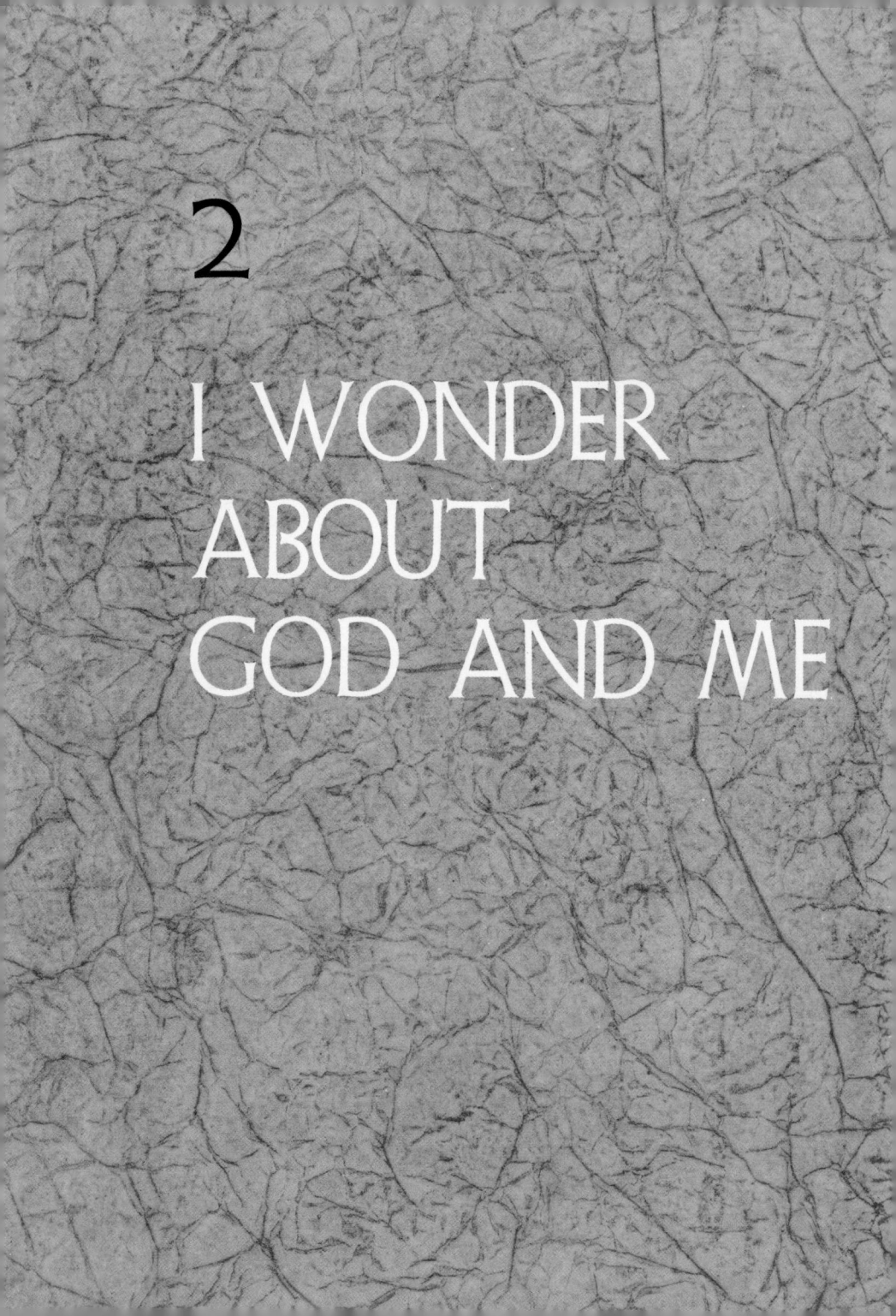

I WONDER ABOUT GOD AND ME

I Wonder If God Knows Me

During the night while Jane was sleeping, the warm weather changed. Grey clouds covered the sky and a cold wind blew. All night long snow fell in big, thick flakes. No one had expected snow so early in the year.

In the morning Jane looked out the window and jumped out of bed. "Yippee!" she shouted. "Saturday and there is snow outside—deep snow!"

Jane liked the snow because it made every place outdoors look different. Then she liked to pretend that she wasn't Jane anymore, but someone different.

After breakfast Jane hurried outside to see how deep the snow was. It came up to her knees and more snow was falling. Snow hid the curbs and sidewalks. Everything as quiet. Only one or two cars had driven past, leaving deep tracks. Everything looked strange and different.

"If I were lost," Jane thought, "and I came here, I wouldn't know this is my street."

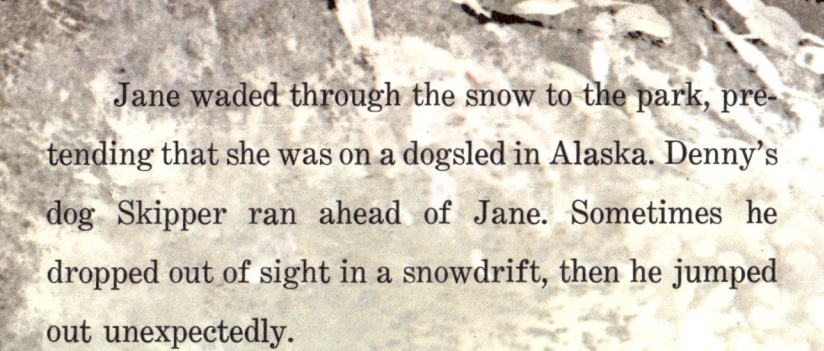

Jane waded through the snow to the park, pretending that she was on a dogsled in Alaska. Denny's dog Skipper ran ahead of Jane. Sometimes he dropped out of sight in a snowdrift, then he jumped out unexpectedly.

"Let's pretend we're Eskimos," Jane said to Skipper. Skipper wagged his tail. "We have to build a snow-house igloo to keep warm."

Jane and Skipper crossed the street at the park. On the corner stood the policeman who said hello to Jane every day on her way to school. He looked at Jane and the dog, but he did not say a word.

"Even the policeman doesn't know me," Jane thought. "I must look like an Eskimo."

Jane figured out how to build an Eskimo igloo. She rolled a snowball this way and that until it was big. Then she made four more big snowballs and put them in a circle with the first one. "It's beginning to look like an Eskimo igloo," she said to Skipper.

Jane made five smaller snowballs and pushed and lifted them up on top of the others. She filled in all the holes with snow and rolled one more snowball for the top.

Jane stood back to look at her igloo. It was still snowing and she was cold and tired, so she crawled inside. She felt warmer at once.

"Here, Skipper, come in and get warm," she called.

Skipper sniffed at the door and crawled in wagging his tail.

Skipper snuggled up close to Jane because the house was very small. She brushed the snow from Skipper. Now she didn't even feel like Jane, who went to school every day and who lived in a real house with her mother and father.

"I feel like a real Eskimo," Jane said to Skipper. "What if I were an Eskimo? I wonder if God really knows me today, down here in my little snow house?"

It's fun to have a secret hiding place where no one knows where you are. It's fun to pretend you aren't you anymore. You can wonder about many things. You can wonder about God and how God can know everybody and how God can always know where you are.

> *O give thanks to the* LORD, *for he is good; for his steadfast love endures for ever!*
> *Psalm 107:1*

If I Weren't Me

Denny and Jane were playing in Denny's yard after school. Skipper came running into the yard. He jumped all around Denny and barked and barked.

"Take it easy, Skipper. I'll feed you pretty soon," Denny said.

Just then a jet plane roared high up in the sky. Denny and Jane looked up to find it. They watched the plane go higher and higher, leaving a white trail across the sky.

"I'd sure like to be a jet pilot," Denny said. "Then I could shoot across the sky as high as I wanted to."

"I'd rather be a pioneer," Jane said. "If I weren't me, I would be a pioneer and ride in a covered wagon across the plains."

"That would be fun," Denny said. "It would be like camping out every night."

"Sometimes I wish I weren't me," Jane said. "Then I wouldn't have to set the table for supper every night."

"If I weren't me," Denny said, "I would be an explorer and discover some country no one had ever seen before. I would be the captain of a ship and sail through storms."

"Then we would have to learn about you in school, like Columbus," Jane said.

"Maybe if I weren't me," Denny said, "I could be a cowboy and ride a horse. And I wouldn't have to do spelling in school."

Jane and Denny were so busy thinking of who they would like to be that they forgot they were really Jane and Denny. Jane forgot all about setting the table. Denny forgot all about feeding Skipper. And he forgot about something he did not like to think about—something he had broken in his big brother's room.

But Skipper didn't forget. He was hungry and ran around and around Denny again and barked to say he wanted his dog food.

"Denny, come in and feed Skipper," called Denny's mother. "It's nearly time for supper."

"I will in a minute," Denny answered.

"I guess I have to go home, too," Jane said. "If I weren't me, who would set the table?"

"See you tomorrow, Jane," Denny said as he went to feed his dog. Skipper raced to beat Denny to the kitchen door.

Then Denny thought about what had happened in his brother's room. He had played with his brother's telescope and had broken a knob. Denny wondered what he should say to his brother—or if he should just keep quiet.

Skipper looked up at Denny and wagged his tail.

Denny smiled. "If I weren't me, Skipper, you would be an awfully hungry dog!"

Then Denny went into the house and thought about how to tell his brother about what had happened to the telescope.

Flying a jet plane is an exciting and important thing to do. It is fun to think about what you might do if you could be someone else. But even if you are just you, you have some things you have to do, too. Sometimes they are hard things to do and sometimes they are things you get tired of doing. God plans useful things for people to do. Denny and Jane remembered things they had to do. What are some of the things you have to do?

3

I WONDER ABOUT WHEN I DO WRONG

"I Will Not Leave You"

The moon shone brightly as Peter and the other disciples walked with Jesus between the spreading branches of the olive trees. There was no sound except their footsteps. Each disciple was silent because everyone was thinking about something that made him feel afraid. Jesus had just told his disciples that he would soon be put to death.

Jesus spoke quietly. "You will all leave me and run away."

Peter looked around at the other disciples. He made a hard fist with his right hand.

"Even if everyone else runs away," Peter said, "I won't." Peter was sure Jesus could count on him.

Jesus stopped and faced Peter. "I tell you, Peter," he said sadly, "this very night—before the rooster crows when night is over—you will say you do not belong to me."

Peter was angry. How could Jesus say that to him! Peter felt how strong the muscles in his arms were. He had big shoulders and his hands were rough from hauling in nets full of fish and pulling heavy boats to shore. He wanted to protect Jesus from any harm.

"Even if I must die with you, I will not leave you," Peter promised. All the other disciples said the same thing. But Jesus did not answer. Together they walked to a quiet place under the olive trees where they often went in the evening. Jesus wanted to pray and asked the disciples to stay awake with him. But soon they fell asleep and even Peter slept.

Jesus woke Peter up. "Could you not stay awake with me?" he asked. "Now the soldiers are coming to arrest me. Come! I must go to them."

Peter saw a crowd of men coming with lanterns and torches and clubs and swords. He wanted to fight and protect Jesus, but Jesus would not let him. So the soldiers took Jesus into the city to a big house where an important official lived. Peter followed in the shadows and kept far enough away so that no one could see him.

"I will find out what they will do to Jesus," Peter said to himself.

Peter saw the door close as the soldiers took Jesus inside the house. Peter waited outside in the courtyard to listen and to watch. The night was very cold so Peter went closer to a fire where soldiers were warming themselves.

A woman came up to Peter and looked at his face. She saw his dark brown hair and suntanned skin. He looked like a fisherman, and his face was crinkly from often squinting into the sunlight on the sea the way fishermen have to do.

The woman knew that many of Jesus' disciples were fishermen. She pointed to Peter and said loud enough for everyone to hear, "You were with that man, Jesus."

Peter was afraid. "I don't know what you mean," he said and hurried out of the courtyard.

The woman looked for Peter and saw him standing by the gate. Again she said loud enough so that all could hear, "That man is one of the friends of Jesus."

"I don't even know the man," Peter said gruffly.

A man in the crowd stepped closer to Peter and looked at him. "Yes, you must be a friend of Jesus.

I know you are, because you come from Galilee where Jesus lived."

"Not me!" Peter shouted. "I never heard of this man you are talking about! I don't know Jesus. He is no friend of mine!"

Far away in the darkness a rooster crowed. Then Peter remembered what Jesus had said to him. He hurried away to be alone, and tears rolled down his cheeks.

Many nights later Peter and some of the disciples were fishing on the lake the way they had done before they knew Jesus. Peter could not forget what had happened after that night when he had said he did not know Jesus. The men had taken Jesus to a cross and had put him to death. Jesus' body had been laid in a grave. Then a strange thing happened: God made Jesus alive again. The disciples had even seen Jesus again for a very short time.

From his boat Peter saw the sun come up over the lake. The time to catch fish was over and they had caught nothing. Suddenly they saw a stranger on the shore who called loudly, "Put down your net over there!" When the disciples dropped their net into the water again, they caught many fish.

When Peter heard the stranger and felt the heavy net full of fish, he wondered, "Can that be Jesus on the shore?" Peter jumped into the water and swam to shore, leaving the other disciples to bring the fishing boat and the net full of fish to land.

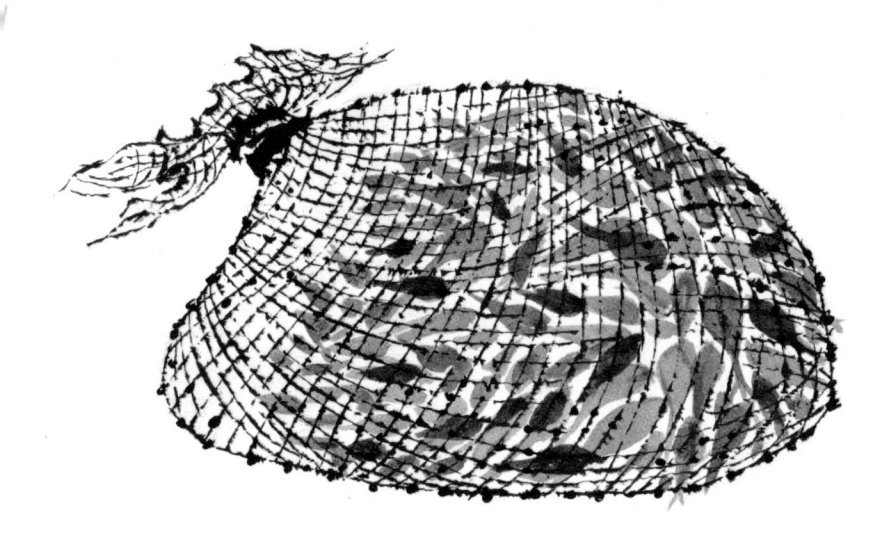

The man on the shore really was Jesus!

Jesus invited the disciples to eat breakfast with him around a fire. After breakfast Jesus turned to Peter and asked, "Peter, do you love me?"

"Yes, Lord, you know that I love you," Peter answered.

"Take care of my people," Jesus said.

Then Jesus asked Peter again, "Peter, do you love me?"

Peter did not brag. He said simply, "Yes, Lord, you know that I love you."

"Take care of my people," Jesus said.

A third time Jesus asked, "Peter, do you love me?"

"Lord, you know everything; you know that I love you," Peter said.

Jesus said to Peter again, "Take care of my people."

Peter was happy again—happier than he had ever been before. He was sure that Jesus still loved him and wanted him to be his helper. Even though Peter had been ashamed and afraid to say he knew Jesus that awful night in the courtyard, Jesus still loved him. Jesus still wanted Peter to be his friend.

God wants his people to do what is good and right. When you say or do nice things, you feel good. But sometimes you say or do things that are mean and ugly. You may wonder if God really loves you when you are bad.

Many people have wondered about times when they have done things they are ashamed of. They have talked with other people about this. They have talked with God, too. A man in the Bible thought and thought about God. Then he said:

> O give thanks to the LORD, for he is good; for his steadfast love endures for ever!
> Psalm 107:1

4

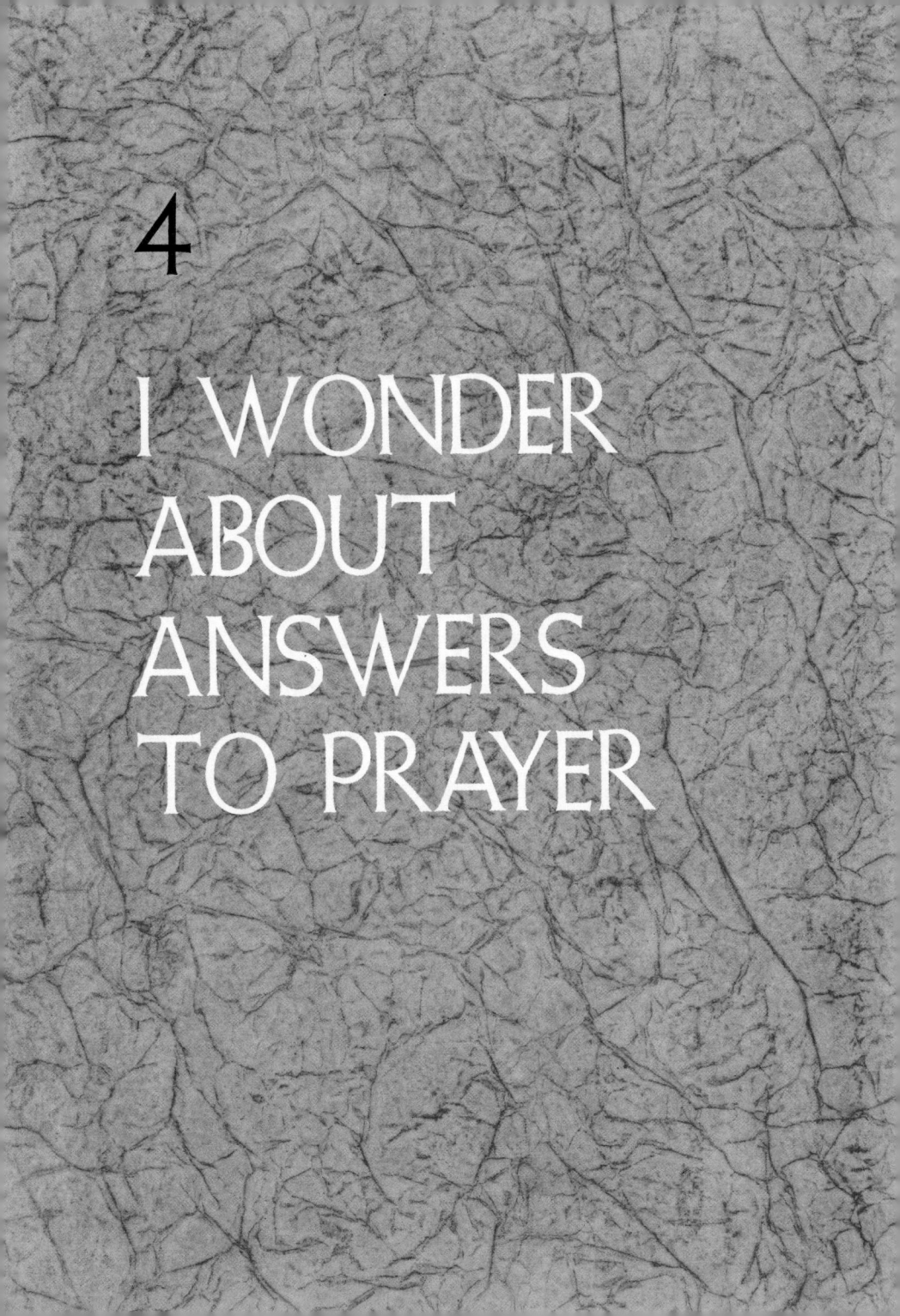

I WONDER ABOUT ANSWERS TO PRAYER

How Jesus Wants Us To Pray

Ever since he was a boy, Peter had prayed. His mother and father had taught him many prayers. But when Peter watched Jesus pray, he saw that Jesus prayed to God in a different way. Peter wished he could pray the way Jesus did.

Peter was with Jesus every day. He often listened to Jesus pray. Sometimes he heard Jesus say the same prayers that Peter had learned from the psalms. Sometimes he heard Jesus say very short prayers. Every prayer of Jesus sounded different. Peter wondered about the right way to pray to God.

One day after Jesus had been praying, one of the disciples turned to Jesus. "Lord," he said, "teach us to pray."

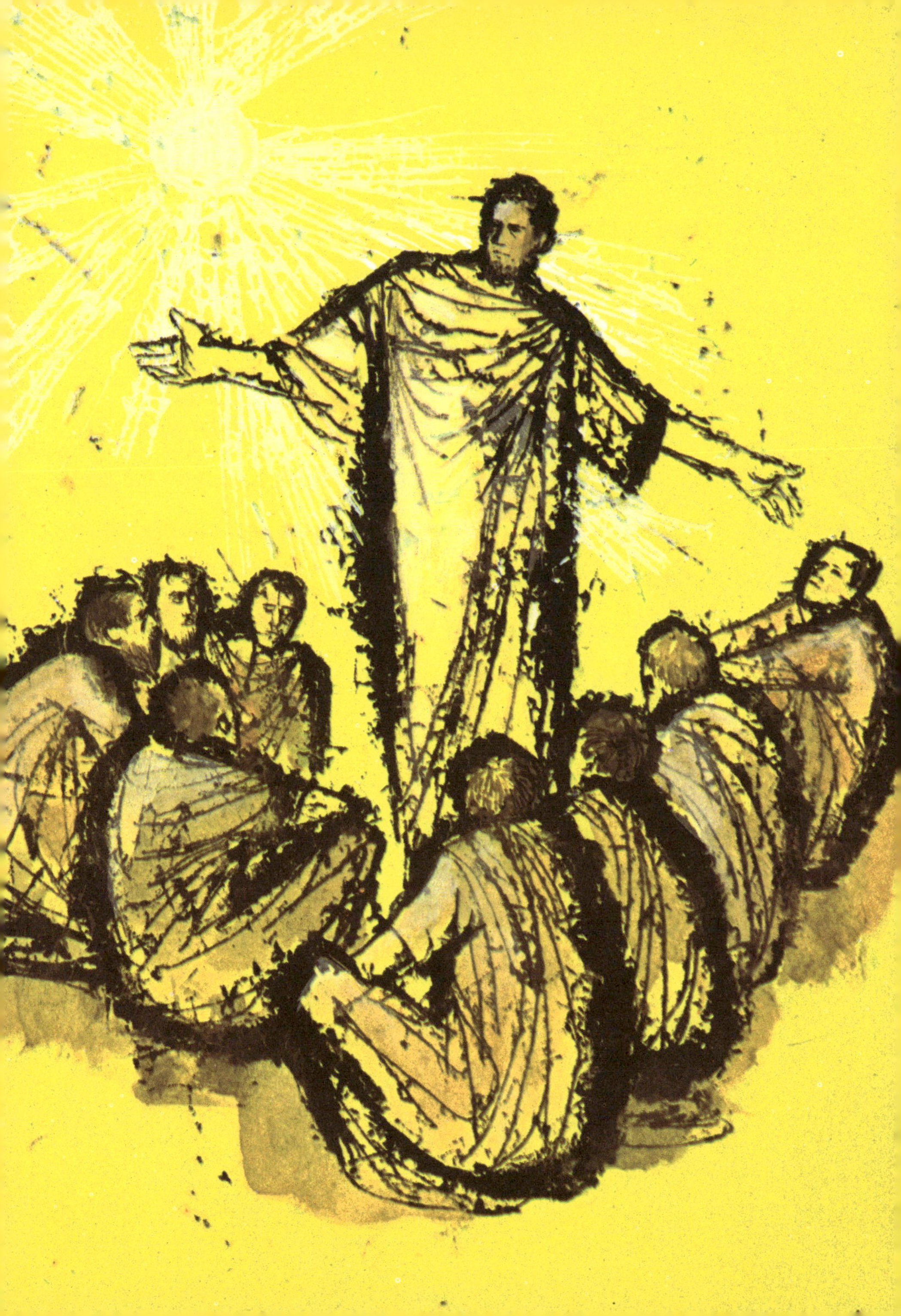

Peter and all the disciples gathered around Jesus. They wanted to hear everything Jesus might tell them about what to pray for and how to pray. Peter hoped he would find out how to pray, so he listened to every word.

Jesus talked about the ways people pray. He said that God knows what we think and how we feel when we pray. He knows what we think no matter what words we say.

Then Jesus told the disciples what they could say when they prayed. "When you pray say:

'Our Father, who art in heaven,

Hallowed be thy Name.

Thy kingdom come,

Thy will be done,

   On earth as it is in heaven.

Give us this day our daily bread;

And forgive us our trespasses,

   As we forgive those who trespass against us;

And lead us not into temptation,

But deliver us from evil.' "

Peter could remember every word because the prayer was short. He was surprised that an important prayer did not have to be long. He had wondered what was different about the way Jesus prayed, and now he understood better. Jesus talked to God as "our Father." Jesus talked to God just the way you talk to someone you know and love very much. Jesus talked to God about a few very important things.

Before Peter went to sleep that night with the disciples he looked up at the stars and prayed to

God. He remembered everything Jesus said. So he prayed Jesus' new prayer.

"Our Father, who art in heaven," Peter began. He said every word that Jesus taught and he thought a long time about what the words meant.

Peter felt happy and close to God. He was learning to talk to God in new and better ways. He was beginning to learn to pray the way Jesus taught him.

The Lord's Prayer is not a prayer that Jesus prayed himself. It is a prayer that Jesus wants us to pray. It helps us to learn about praying because it tells us some important things to pray for. We will always need to learn how to pray better, even when we are grown up. We can begin as Peter did by thinking of how God loves us all as a kind and loving Father. Then we can think of the things we need to tell God when we pray.

Wondering About God

I WONDER about God and the little baby. Once I was a little baby and I wonder how God makes a baby's tiny hands and feet. I know that God loves every mother and every baby.

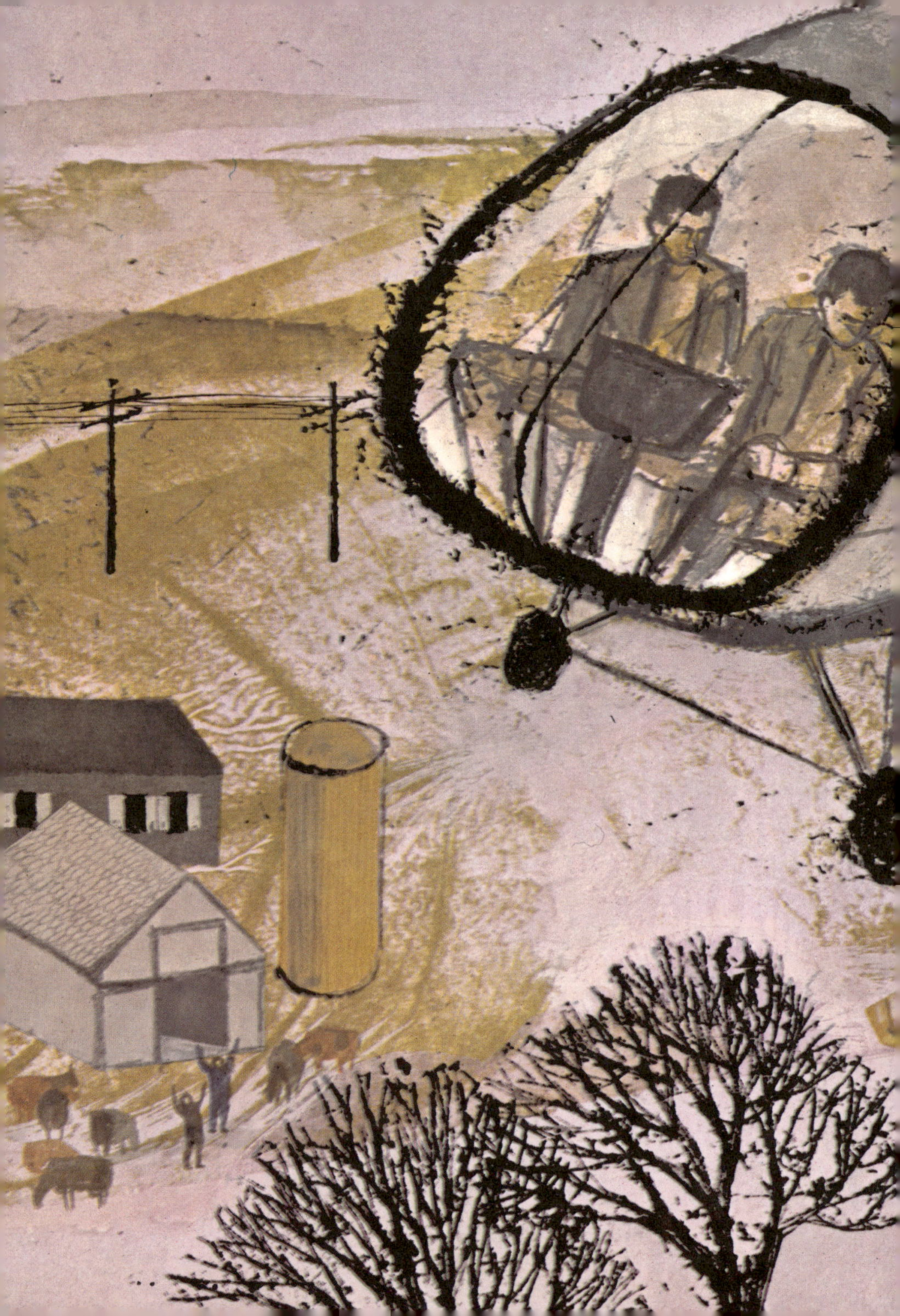

I WONDER why God lets bad things like storms and floods happen. I am glad that we have helicopters and brave pilots, radio and special medicines to help people quickly. God wants us to use the things we have to help people.

I WONDER how God can hear all the people when they pray to him at the same time. This is something I cannot understand, but I know that God is so great that he can do things people cannot understand or explain.

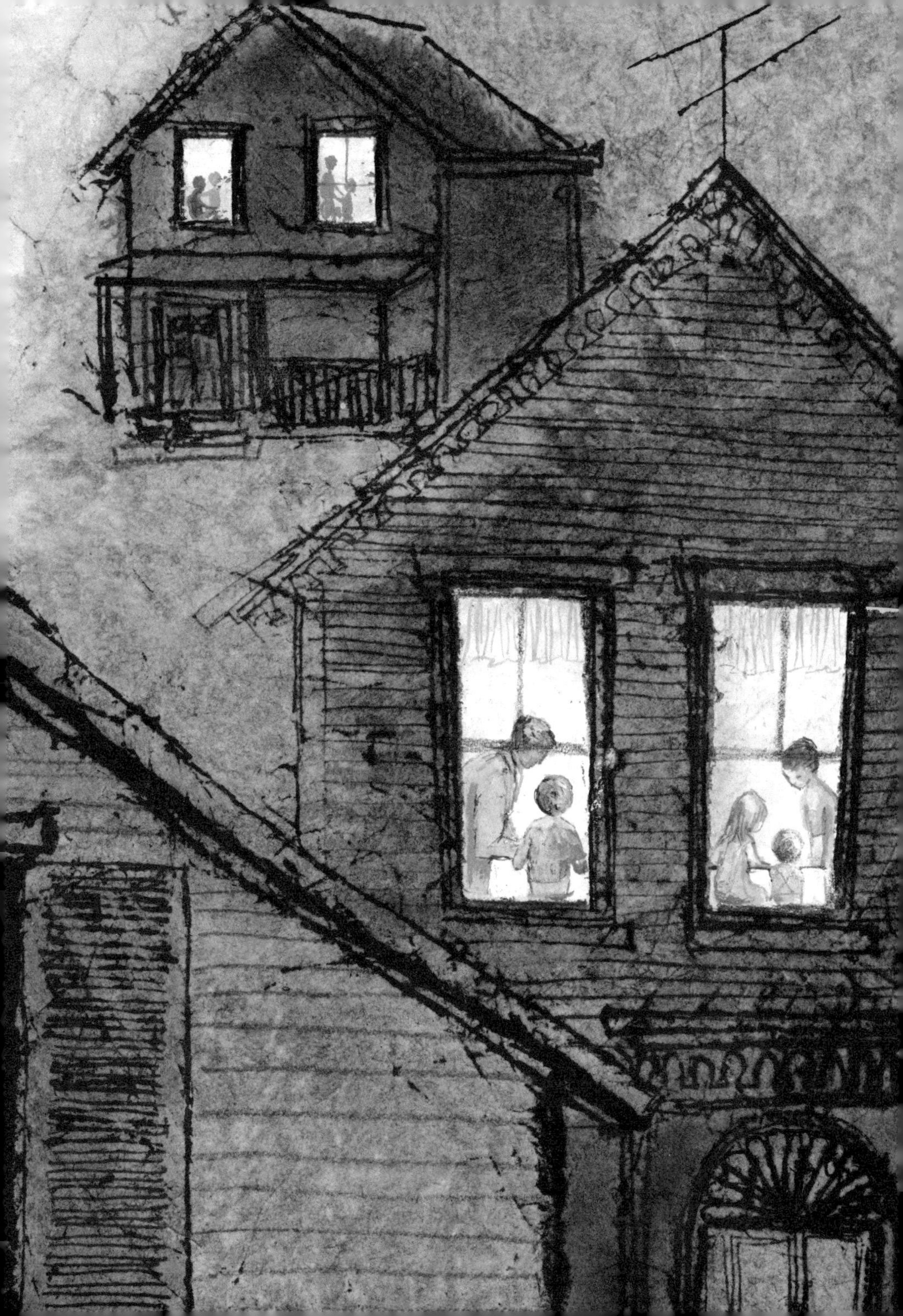

Make Someone Stop

Linda was riding to the store with her mother and looking out of the car window. Suddenly she saw a dog start to run across the street.

"Look out!" shouted Linda. "There's a dog running right in front of our car!"

Linda's mother slammed on the brakes and turned the car so that she missed the dog.

"It's all right," Linda's mother said. "We didn't hit the dog."

Linda saw how scared the dog was. It turned to run back to the sidewalk. Just then a car came from the other direction and hit the dog. Linda heard the dog yelp and saw him crawl to the curb. The car that hit the dog did not stop.

"Please, dear God," Linda's mother prayed silently, "make someone stop and help that dog. Please, God, make someone stop."

Linda watched out the back window. "Nobody stopped to help the dog," she said.

Linda's mother knew that she had to help. She turned at the next corner and drove around the block.

"We're going to go back to help the dog," she said.

A small boy was sitting beside the dog when Linda and her mother drove up. He was crying.

"A car hit Boots," he sobbed.

Linda's mother knelt by the dog. One of his back legs was cut and bleeding.

"Go and get your mother," Linda's mother said, "and I will hold the dog."

She petted the dog's head and talked to him softly.

"Hold still, Boots," she said, "while I fix your leg." Linda's mother tied a handkerchief around the dog's leg to stop the bleeding. The dog whimpered.

"Will the dog die?" Linda asked.

"I hope not," her mother answered.

The boy hurried back with his mother. "Oh, poor Boots," the boy's mother said. "It looks as if he was hurt badly, Timothy."

"A car hit him and drove away," Linda's mother explained. "Do you want to take Boots to a veterinarian? We can drive you there."

Linda's mother drove quickly to the veterinarian's office. Timothy's mother carried Boots carefully into the office. Linda and her mother and Timothy went in, too. They all waited while the doctor laid the dog on the table and looked at his leg. Timothy was crying because it was his dog and he was worried about him.

"The dog has a deep cut on his leg," the doctor said, "but no bone is broken. I will bandage him up and give him a shot to help him sleep. We'll keep him here in the animal hospital overnight. You can probably take him home tomorrow."

Timothy stopped crying and ran to Boots. He put his arms around the dog and hugged him.

"It's a good thing you brought this dog in right away," said the doctor. "He might have died if you hadn't."

Linda's mother remembered that she had prayed to God to make someone stop and help. "Thank you, dear God," she prayed silently. "Thank you for making me stop to help."

Linda's mother, a car, a handkerchief, a doctor, good medicine—all these things helped the little dog, Boots. When we pray to God, God wants us to use things we have in our world to help. And God cares about every one of his creatures.

In God's hand is the life of every living thing. Job 12:10

5

I WONDER WHY CHRISTIANS ARE GLAD AT CHRISTMAS

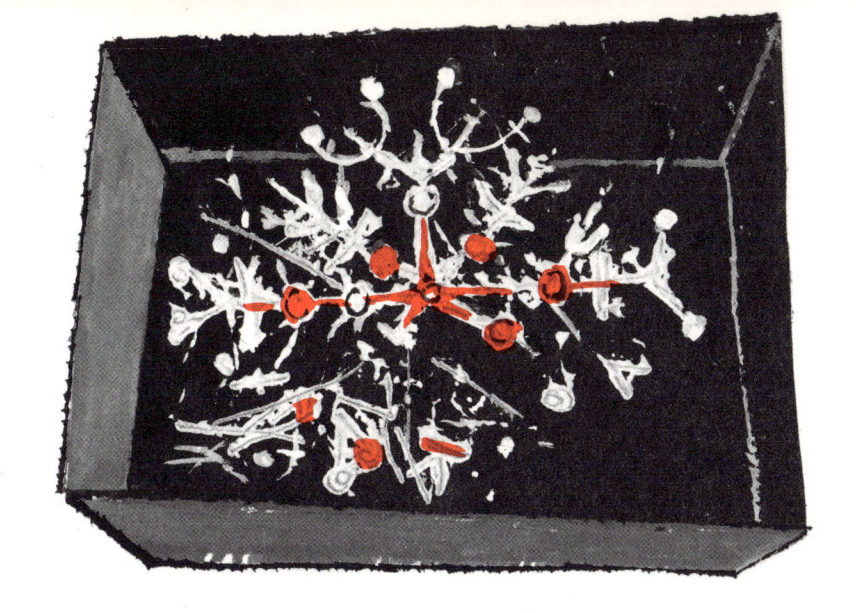

The Broken Star

Everyone in Debbie's house was getting ready for Christmas Eve. Debbie and her two sisters were helping to decorate the Christmas tree. Father was standing on a stepladder to fix a burned-out light. Mother was opening boxes of shiny red and gold ornaments. The sisters were hanging tinsel.

"Oh, look what happened!" Mother said. "Our star for the top of the tree is broken." Mother picked the broken pieces out of the box. "It's broken into too many pieces to be fixed and it's too late to get a new one."

Debbie looked at the broken pieces. "That star was always the best thing on our tree," she said. "It was so pretty and bright. It made me think of the first Christmas star—the one that shone over the place where the baby Jesus was."

"Too bad it's broken," Father said as he climbed down from the stepladder. "I guess we'll have to get along without it this year."

As Debbie hung the sparkling balls on the tree, she looked at each one and wondered, "Can we put this one at the top instead of our star?" But each time she thought, "No, that wouldn't look right. We need a star like the one at the first Christmas."

Finally the tree was finished except for the bare top where the star belonged. No one had found an ornament that was right. Debbie thought and thought. "We have to have a star, but how?"

"I know!" Debbie said. "I have an idea!"

"What is it?" her mother asked.

"I can't tell, but it is going to be something for our tree," Debbie answered. She hurried to the kitchen and found a roll of aluminum foil and a pair of scissors. She tore off a piece of shiny foil and cut out a star. It had only four points.

"That is not good enough," Debbie said to herself. "The one over the baby Jesus must have been very special—not all crooked and funny the way this one is."

Debbie cut out another star. This one had five points, but it wasn't very even. So she cut out another star.

"That is a good one," Debbie said. She was pleased with what she had made.

And then since this was going to be a very special star, she cut out two more stars just like the good one. Debbie held the three stars together and punched a hole through the middle with her scissors. The hole was for the light bulb. Then Debbie cut out a small piece of cardboard, punched a hole in it, and pasted her stars on it. Now her surprise was ready.

Debbie peeked out through the kitchen doorway to see if anyone was still in the room with the Christmas tree. Only Father was there, reading the paper. Debbie went into the living room, holding the star behind her back.

Keeping the star hidden from her father, Debbie climbed up the stepladder to the third step. She looked up to the top of the tree, but it was too far above her head to reach.

"I guess you'll have to hang up my surprise, Daddy," Debbie said. She held up her star.

"Why, that's a good star, Debbie!" he said.

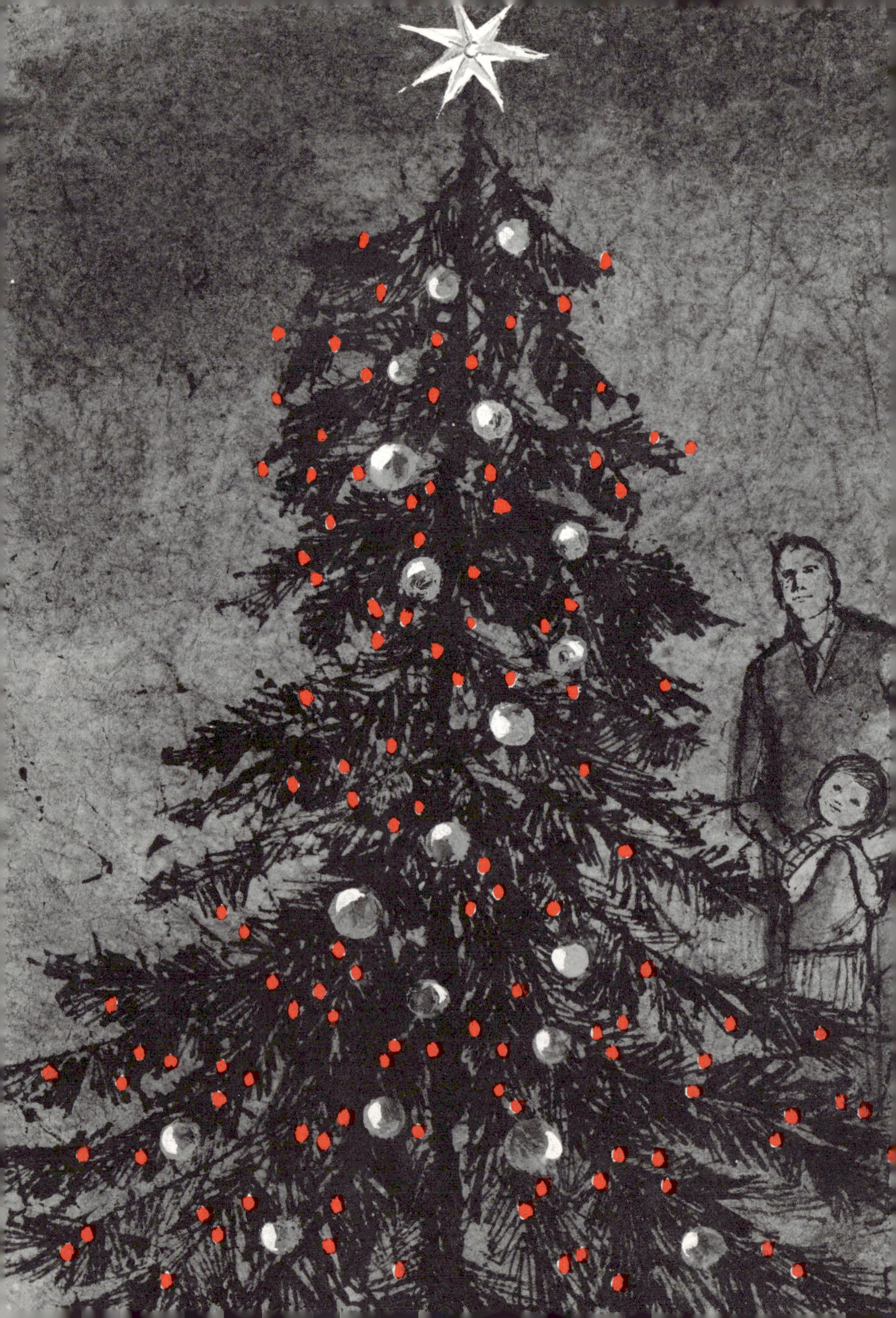

Then he came to help her. He took the star up the ladder with him and slipped it carefully around a white light bulb on the tip of the tree. Then he climbed down and took the ladder away so they could admire the star.

Father switched off the other lights in the room and put his arm around Debbie. In the darkness the tree sparkled with lights and tinsel.

"It's beautiful," Debbie said softly.

"And the star is exactly what we needed," Father said.

There are different ways you can help get ready for Christmas at home. It is fun to enjoy what you helped to do and what other people have done to get ready for Christmas. When we think at Christmas about the coming of Jesus we want to show our love.

The LORD *is good to all. Psalm 145:9*

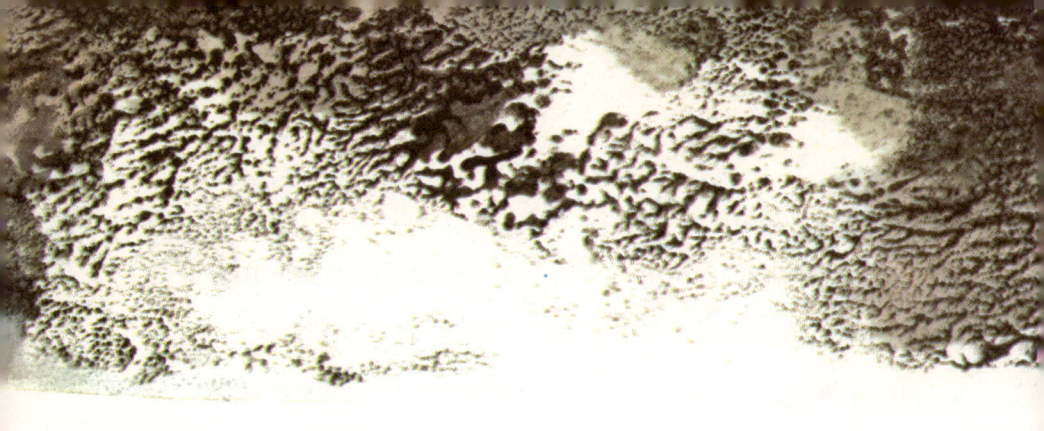

God's Angel Told Us

Out on a hill near the little town of Bethlehem a young shepherd was taking care of a flock of sheep. Tonight was his turn to stay awake and guard the sheep while the other shepherds slept. He rubbed his hands together and stamped his feet to keep warm.

High above, stars shone brightly, but suddenly the shepherd saw a light that was brighter than all the stars in the sky. The light grew larger and brighter.

The young shepherd ran to the oldest shepherd and shook him awake.

"Wake up! Wake up!" he shouted. "Something is coming close to our sheep. Look—the light! It is far from morning, but the sky is getting bright."

The oldest shepherd blinked his eyes. The light was so bright he could hardly see anything else.

"I have never seen anything like this before," he said. The old man shook with fear.

The light became so bright now that it woke up the other shepherds. They did not know what to do or how to protect their sheep against this strange light. In the center of the brightness they saw an angel. Never before had the shepherds seen an angel of God and that made them even more afraid.

The sheep bleated and huddled close together. A young shepherd boy ran to his father to be safe. Another shepherd threw himself behind a big rock and hid his face from the bright light. The oldest shepherd stayed with the sheep and raised his staff to protect himself.

"Be not afraid," the angel said. "I bring you good news of a great joy which will come to all the people; for to you is born this day a Savior who is Christ the Lord. You will know that I am telling the truth by something that has just happened in the town of Bethlehem. You will find a new baby wrapped in swaddling clothes and lying in a manger. When you see him, you will know that the good news is true."

More angels came until the sky was full of them. The sky grew even brighter as the angels sang a song of praise to God. Then the angels disappeared and the light faded away.

The shepherds watched silently. Finally one of them said, "An angel of God really talked to us!" He could hardly believe it was true. "An angel of God! And we are only shepherds."

"Let's go to Bethlehem and see the wonderful thing that has happened," the oldest shepherd said to the others.

"Let's hurry!" the shepherd boy said.

The shepherds led their sheep into a safe place. Then they ran across the fields to get to the town of Bethlehem as quickly as they could.

There, in Bethlehem, just as the angel had told them, they found Joseph and Mary. And they did find a new baby lying in a manger.

"It is true! God has sent this baby and here he is, a little baby in a manger!" the old shepherd said.

The oldest shepherd turned to Joseph. "An angel told us about this new baby," he said.

"God's angel told us that this baby will make many people happy," the young boy said.

"Yes," said Joseph, "and the baby's name is Jesus."

When the shepherds had told Mary and Joseph all about the light in the sky and the angels, they went back to their sheep.

Morning had come. On the way back to the fields the shepherds met people going to and from the town. "Something wonderful has happened to you tonight. The Lord has been born!"

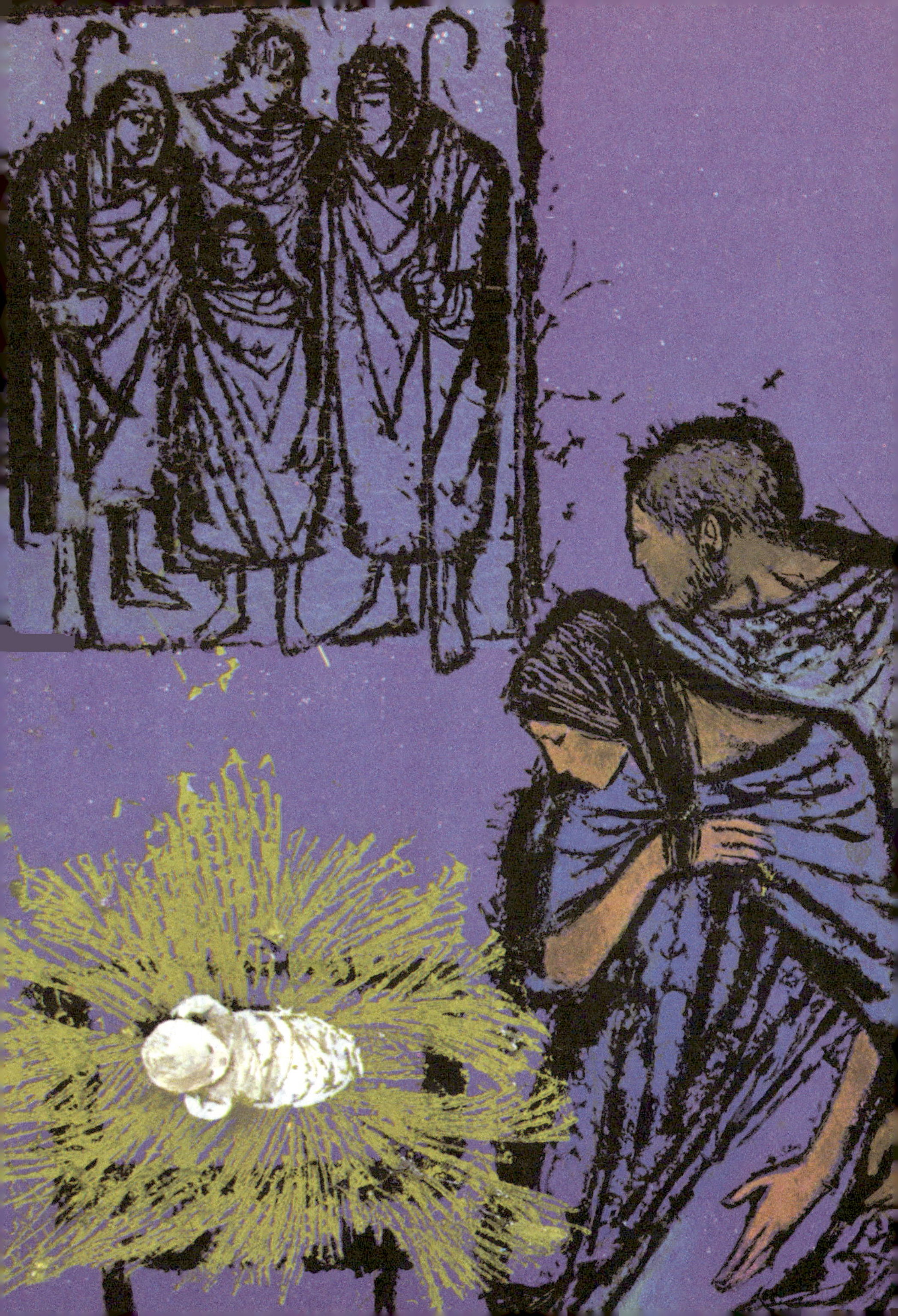

"Where is he?" people asked. "Can we see him?"

"He is in the manger over there," the shepherds answered, "just as God's angel told us."

The shepherds wanted to tell everyone about the good news. Some people just shook their heads and wondered if the shepherds knew what they were talking about. Others hurried to see the new baby.

The sun shone brightly when the shepherds got back to their sheep. "God is good to us," they said. "He has sent us a baby who will grow to do wonderful things for the people!"

There is a Bible verse which is good to remember and use at Christmastime. Maybe you can say it without reading it.

> *The angel said to them, "Be not afraid; for behold, I bring you good news of a great joy." Luke 2:10*

The King's Star

In a land far to the east across the desert lived some wise men. It was their business to watch the sky and to study the stars. One day one of the wise men saw something new in the sky. "See," he said, "there is a bright, new star in the sky."

Every night the wise men studied the new star. It was the brightest star in the sky and they wondered why it was there.

"I think I know what the new star means," one of the wise men said. "In an old, old book it is written that God will send a new king to be born in Judea, the land of the Jewish people. He will become a great and important person. This new star must be the star of that king."

"I have read about this king who will come," said another wise man. "I think that the star does point to the land of Judea."

"We must find out about the star," said the oldest wise man. "We must go across the desert to Judea to see the new king."

The wise men decided to leave their books and their comfortable houses. They packed food and clothes and loaded their camels. The best camel drivers were chosen for the long journey.

Finally a line of camels carrying the wise men, their servants, and their belongings started across the desert. Each wise man had extra camels to carry his clothes and blankets and tent. And all the wise men had chosen very precious gifts to give to the new king.

The long line of camels traveled in the desert at night after the hot sun had gone down and it was cool. By day they rested in their tents. Traveling across the desert was hard and the wise men became very tired. Often there was not enough water to drink. Strong winds blew sand in their faces and mouths. At night it was very cold and by day it was very hot, much too hot to sleep.

"Oh, how good a cool bath would be," said the youngest wise man. "Maybe we should turn back."

"It might be a very foolish idea to try to follow that star," said another wise man. "Can we be sure what it means?"

But the oldest wise man would not give up. "We are going to see the great, new king. We should not give up and turn back."

After many days of travel the wise men came to stony hills. They climbed the hills with their camels and saw in the distance a large city with a thick stone wall around it.

"That is the city of Jerusalem, the biggest city in Judea. We are nearly there."

They rode their camels through the gates of the city to the great house of Herod, who was king of Judea.

"We have came to worship the new king," the wise men explained to Herod. "Where is he?"

Herod frowned. He thought that he was the king of Judea. Was there someone who wanted to be king in his place? Herod asked his own wise men. They said that there was a promise in the Bible that one day God would send a new king to be born in Bethlehem. So Herod told the wise men to go to Bethlehem to find out.

The wise men rode their camels south to Bethlehem. Again they saw the bright star. "We must be on the right road," they said.

When the wise men got to Bethlehem, they found the house where Joseph and Mary lived and where the new child Jesus was. The wise men got off their camels and knelt down to show their love.

"This child will grow up to be the great, new king God is sending us. We followed his star here."

The wise men brought their gifts to Jesus and laid them down for him to see. They were the kind of presents to give to a king: shining gold, sweet-smelling frankincense, precious myrrh.

"We have come a long way," said the wise men, "and we are glad to show our love to this child."

"I am glad we did not turn back in the desert," said one of the wise men, "for now we have seen the new king."

We hang up stars at Christmas to remember the wise men. A verse in the Bible tells what the wise men said:

"We have seen his star in the East, and have come to worship him." Matthew 2:2

6

I WONDER ABOUT THINGS NOBODY TELLS ME

What God Looks Like

One by one the disciples and Jesus climbed up the narrow stone steps. At the top they opened a heavy wooden door and went into a clean, quiet room. After they sat down, everyone was still. The disciples were worried because for a long time Jesus seemed so sad. He did not smile as much as he used

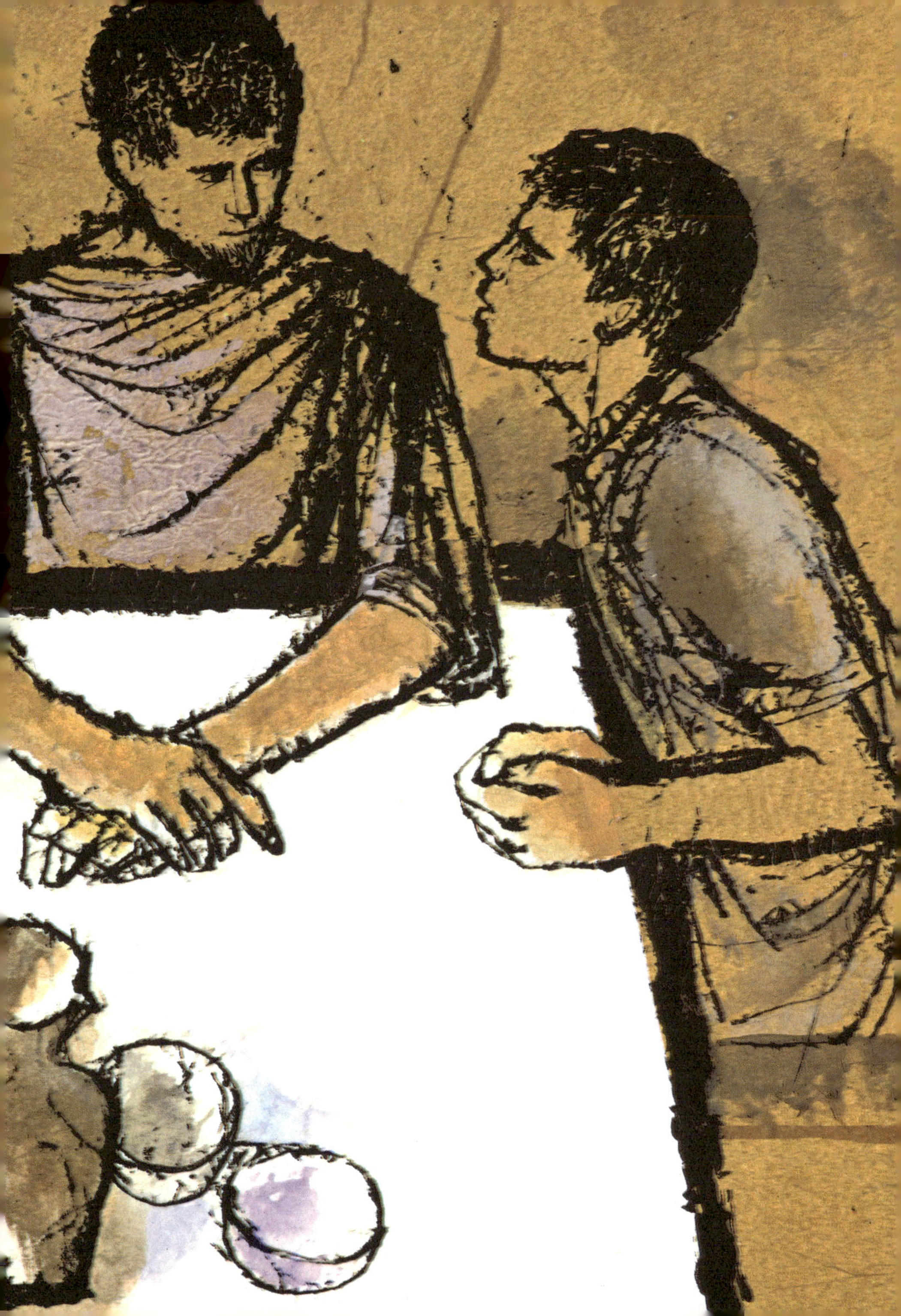

to. He seemed to be thinking very hard about something. Sometimes he closed his eyes to think harder.

Jesus looked around at his friends. He counted them; all twelve men were there. With the disciples, Jesus ate a special meal such as Jewish people eat on the festival days called the Passover.

After the meal, Jesus explained that he would soon have to go away from his friends. He would go away to be with God, and the disciples could not go with him there.

The disciples shook their heads. They could not understand.

"Lord, where are you going?" Peter asked.

"Lord, we do not know where you are going," said Thomas.

No one could understand what Jesus meant when he said he would go away to be with God. Even though Jesus had said, "Let not your hearts be troubled," the disciples were still worried. They wanted Jesus to explain what he meant, but they did not know what questions to ask.

One of the disciples was a young man named Philip. He wondered what Jesus meant when he said that they could not go with him when he would go away. Philip wondered how Jesus could go to be with God. He wondered about God and the things Jesus said about God the Father.

Finally Philip said plainly, "Lord, show us the Father and we shall be satisfied."

Philip wanted Jesus to tell him just what God is like. He wanted to know what God looks like and where God is. He wanted Jesus to tell him and all his friends very plainly about God.

Jesus looked into Philip's eyes. He understood why Philip asked the question.

"You should know the answer to your question by now," Jesus said. "You should know what God is like."

Now every disciple listened very carefully. They were all thinking about the question Philip had asked. They all wanted to know more about God. They wished they could see God and that they could understand God better.

"You know me, do you not?" Jesus asked.

Philip nodded his head. He knew Jesus very well because he was one of Jesus's best friends. He was a disciple.

"If you know me and if you know what I am like," Jesus explained, "then you know already what God is like."

Philip and the disciples thought about what Jesus said. They knew that God was not a man who wore a beard the way Jesus did. God did not wear clothes and eat and sleep and work the way Jesus did. But they began to understand that God was like Jesus—all that Jesus said and did helped them know God better.

Jesus loved everybody. He loved the poor. He loved people who were not liked by anyone else. He liked children and wanted to protect them. He helped all kinds of people. He helped Philip and the other disciples learn how to live as God wanted them to do.

The more Philip thought about it, the more he began to understand that even if he could not see God, he knew much about God because he knew what Jesus was like and what Jesus did.

God cannot be seen, but sometimes artists try to draw pictures to help people think about God. They may show him as an old man with a kind face and a long, white beard. That is the way some artists show that God is very important and very wise. But this does not mean that God looks like an old man. No one can take a picture of God. But if we know and love Jesus well, we can be sure that we will learn to know God better.

> *Jesus said, "He who has seen me has seen the Father." John 14:8*

How Jesus' Promise Comes True

Some of the words for God are hard to understand. Of course, you know about GOD, and about JESUS CHRIST, but there is another name for God. It is the HOLY SPIRIT. Jesus made a special promise about the Holy Spirit. You can start with that promise to find out what Holy Spirit means and what he does today.

Jesus told his disciples that he would have to leave them. No one would be able to see him anymore. Jesus blessed his disciples: "Peace I leave with you; my peace I give to you. . . . Let not your hearts be troubled, neither let them be afraid."

But the disciples were afraid. They did not know what they would do without Jesus. They did not understand the promise of Jesus. Jesus promised that when he would go away, God would send the Holy Spirit. "He will teach you all things," Jesus said. But the disciples did not understand this promise.

"What is the Holy Spirit," the disciples wondered.

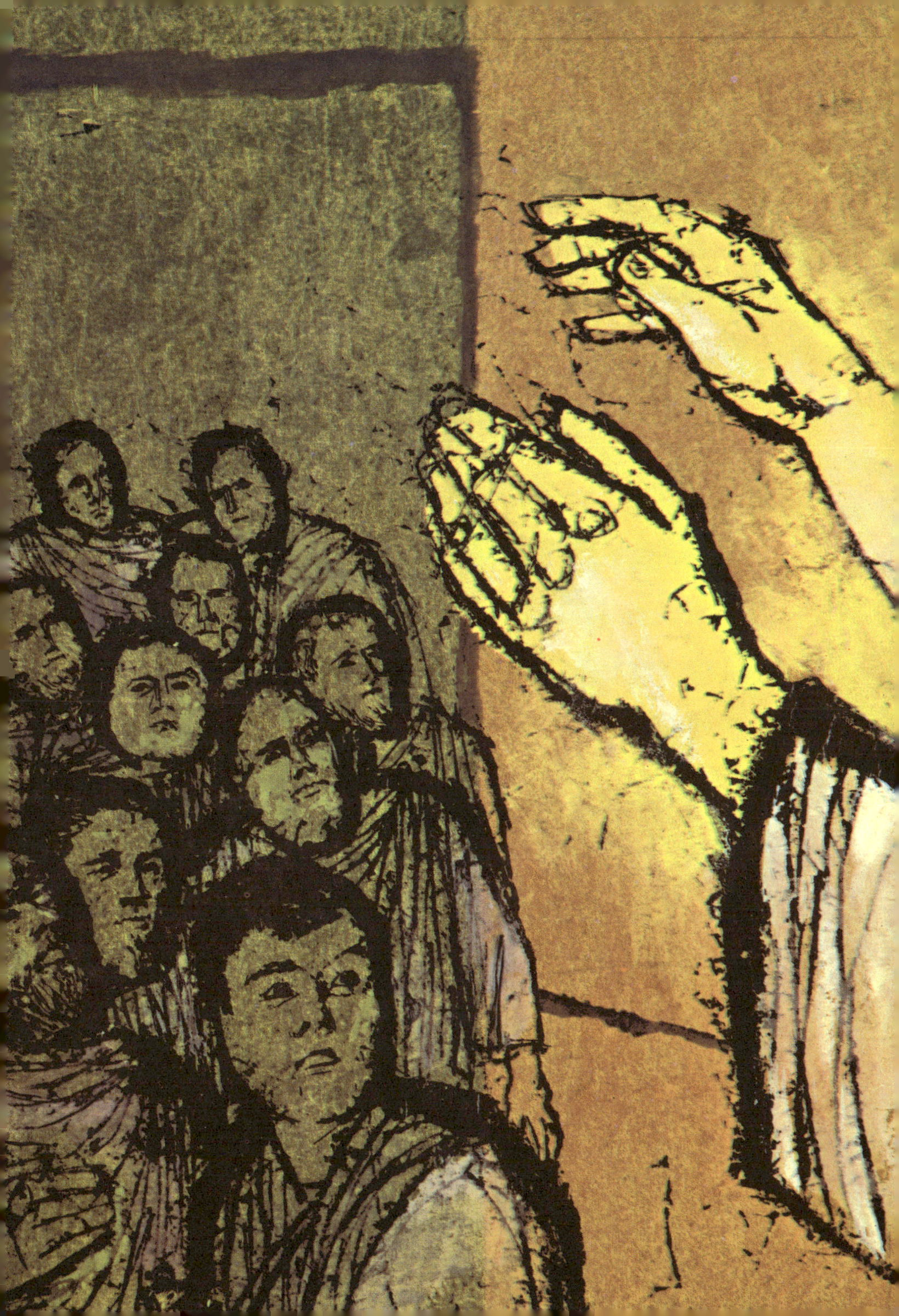

After Jesus had died on the cross and had risen again, the disciples waited. They wondered when Jesus' promise about the Holy Spirit would come true. Then on a festival day called Pentecost, Peter stood up boldly and told the people about Jesus. The enemies of Jesus wanted to stop Peter, but he was not afraid. He became a brave speaker for Jesus because the Holy Spirit helped him.

The Holy Spirit helps people be brave for Jesus. When men and women risk danger to help people know and love Jesus, the Holy Spirit helps them. He helps them not to be afraid. He helps them to know what to say and do.

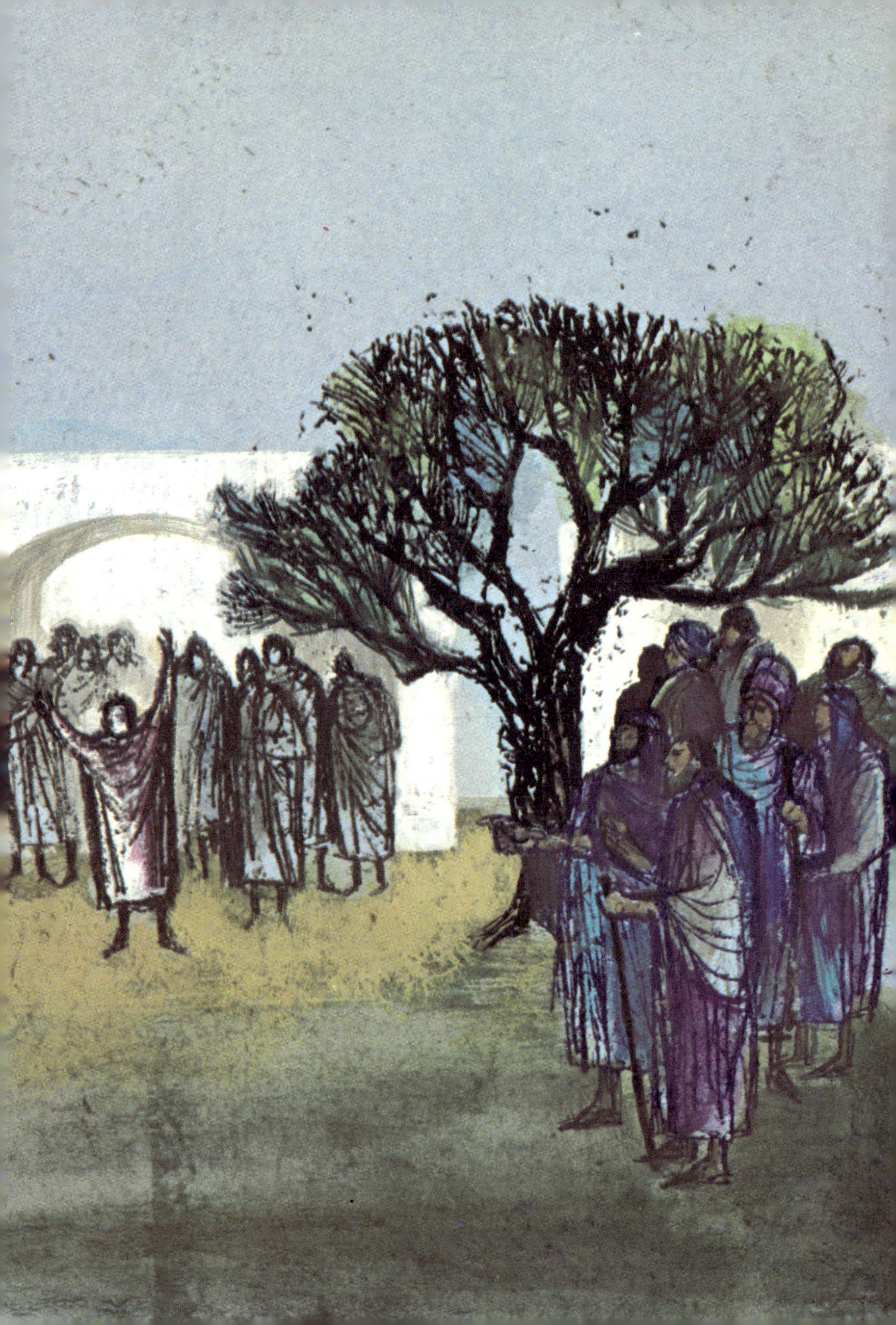

Father handles the Bible carefully because he knows that it is a special book that helps us know God.

"What are you going to read from the Bible today?" Mother asks.

"Just a minute," Father says. "I want to find a happy psalm because this is a happy day."

Whenever we use the Bible carefully and try to study and understand it, the Holy Spirit helps us. He helps us understand God better by using the Bible.

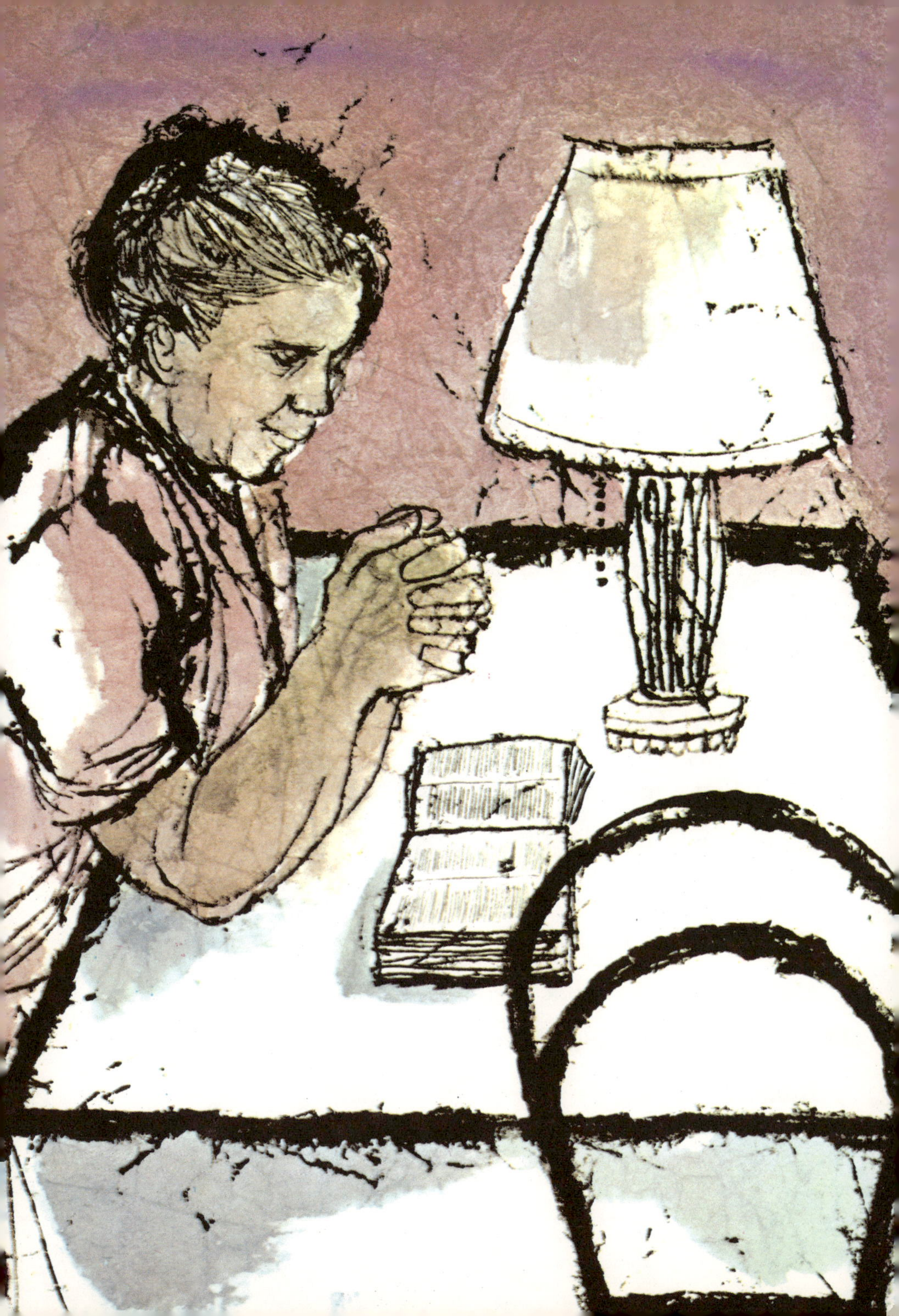

Grandmother folds her hands and closes her eyes to pray. She did that when she was a child and she still does it now when she is old. She knows that she can talk to God even without saying a word aloud and that God will know everything in her prayer. Most important, the Holy Spirit helps her when she prays.

The Holy Spirit helps every friend of Jesus to pray. He helps us in the way we feel inside and in choosing the things we talk about in our prayers. We may not know that the Holy Spirit is with us, but Jesus promised that even though we cannot see the Spirit he will always help those who want to love and serve God.

I Wonder About Heaven

It was Saturday morning. Denny and Jane were playing on the sidewalk in front of Denny's house. They were taking turns trying to walk on the stilts Denny's father had made for him.

"Whew! I'm tired!" Denny put down the stilts and sat on the front step beside Jane.

"Something smells good," said Jane. "Your mother must be baking cookies."

"No, that's my grandmother baking chocolate brownies," said Denny. "She's staying here until my mother comes home. My mother had to go to Chicago because my Uncle Jack died."

"Oh . . ." Jane was quiet for a minute. "When Grandma Mason died, I stayed with Aunt Ellen."

Now Denny was quiet for a minute. Then he said, "I liked my Uncle Jack because he was lots of fun. But I won't see him any more. He's in heaven now."

"In heaven!" exclaimed Jane. "Grandma Mason is in the cemetery. We put flowers on her grave."

"My mother said that Uncle Jack is in heaven," insisted Denny. "And what she says is right!"

"I don't think there really is any place like heaven," said Jane. "Men have been way up high in space ships, and I'll bet they never saw any heaven!"

"There is, too, a heaven. . . ." Denny was beginning to be worried and a bit angry.

Just then Jane's mother called, "Time to come for lunch!" And off went Jane without another word.

119

Denny sat alone for a few minutes—just thinking. Then very slowly he went into the house.

Grandmother was taking a pan of brownies out of the oven. "There!" she said. "The brownies are all baked. I'll get a sandwich and a glass of milk, and then you can have chocolate brownies for dessert."

She looked at Denny. "Why, Denny, what a solemn face! Is something wrong?"

"No . . . nothing . . ." Denny mumbled. Then suddenly he burst out, "Grandma, it *is* true, isn't it? There *is* a heaven just like Mother says, isn't there? Jane says there isn't any place like heaven!"

Grandmother sat down so she could look right into Denny's face. "Of course, there is a heaven, Denny," she said. "We know there is because Jesus told his friends that they would be there with him."

"Then where is it?" Denny wanted to know. "Is it higher than space?"

"That's a harder question to answer," said Grandmother. "Heaven is not a place that you can find . . . like your house . . . or Chicago. Heaven is different from our earth."

"Then what is it like? Wouldn't there be houses and people and streets?" Denny had lots of questions to ask.

"We don't know that either," Grandmother answered. "But we do know that God's love goes on even when we die. You know that God loves you today. And you know, too, that God will love you tomorrow, even if you don't know now what you will do tomorrow. In the same way, even if we don't know where heaven is and what it looks like, we can be sure it will be good because God loves us."

"And if Jesus is there, it must be a good place," said Denny.

"That's right," smiled Grandmother. "I think so, too. And now let's have some lunch."

"Sure, let's hurry," Denny said, "Right after lunch I want to tell Jane."

Jesus said, "Let not your hearts be troubled . . . where I am you may be also."
John 14:1, 3

Songs and Prayers

God knows each shining star,
And all across the night
No planet, near or far,
Is hidden from his sight.

Though rockets disappear
In miles of outer space,
God sees them, bright and clear,
God is in every place.

—Victoria Saffelle Johnson

All Things Bright and Beautiful

All things bright and beautiful,
All creatures great and small,
All things wise and wonderful,
The Lord God made them all.

Each little flower that opens,
Each little bird that sings,
He made their glowing colors,
He made their tiny wings.

He gave us eyes to see them,
And lips that we might tell
How great is God Almighty,
Who has made all things well.
　　　　—Cecil Frances Alexander

A PRAYER FOR GOD TO BE NEAR

Be with us, Lord, in trouble;
Be with us in our play.
Help us, O Lord, to worship you
And praise you every day. Amen.
—Betty M. Getman

A PRAYER AT BREAKFAST TIME

For each new morning with its light,
For rest and shelter of the night,
For food and health, for love and friends,
For everything your goodness sends,
Thank you, God our Father.
—Ralph Waldo Emerson, adapted

A PRAYER FOR FORGIVENESS

Dear God, Thank you for forgiving us when we do things that are wrong. Help us to forgive others. Amen.

A PRAYER ABOUT GOD'S LOVE FOR ME

God cares for me in many ways
This is how I know:
The food I eat,
The clothes I wear,
Friendly helpers everywhere
Say, "You are in God's care."

God shows his love in many ways
This is how I know:
Friendly smiles,
Loving words, and
Pleasant things to do
Say, "God is love. He cares for you."

I must give my thanks to God
For all the love he shows:
For food to eat,
Clothes to wear,
For friendly helpers everywhere.
Dear God, I give my thanks!
—Eleanor Zimmerman

ACKNOWLEDGMENTS

Grateful acknowledgment is made to the following for permission to use material copyrighted by them: Victoria Saffelle Johnson for "God Knows Each Shining Star." Augustana Book Concern for "A Prayer at Breakfast Time" adapted from a poem by Ralph Waldo Emerson in *Children of the Heavenly Father*. The Seabury Press, Inc. for "A Prayer for God to Be Near," by Betty M. Getman, reprinted from *Sing for Joy*, © 1961. Augsburg Publishing House for "A Prayer for Forgiveness" from *Kindergarten Teacher's Guide*, Bible Storytime Series, Year 1.

Scripture quotations are from the *Revised Standard Version of the Bible*, copyrighted 1946 and 1952 by the Division of Christian Education, National Council of Churches, and are used by permission.